THE BOOK OF

Psalms 101-150

ONE CHAPTER A DAY

GoodMorningGirls.org

Psalms 101–150

Welcome to Good Morning Girls! We are so glad you are joining us.

God created us to walk with Him, to know Him, and to be loved by Him. He is our living well, and when we drink from the water He continually provides, His living water will change the entire course of our lives.

Jesus said: "Whoever drinks of the water that I will give him will never be thirsty again. The water that I will give him will become in him a spring of water welling up to eternal life." ~ John 4:14 (ESV)

So let's begin.

The method we use here at GMG is called the **SOAK** method.

- ❏ **S**—The S stands for *Scripture*—Read the chapter for the day. Then choose 1-2 verses and write them out word for word. (There is no right or wrong choice—just let the Holy Spirit guide you.)

- ❏ **O**—The O stands for *Observation*—Look at the verse or verses you wrote out. Write 1 or 2 observations. What stands out to you? What do you learn about the character of God from these verses? Is there a promise, command or teaching?

- ❏ **A**—The A stands for *Application*—Personalize the verses. What is God saying to you? How can you apply them to your life? Are there any changes you need to make or an action to take?

- ❏ **K**—The K stands for *Kneeling in Prayer*—Pause, kneel and pray. Confess any sin God has revealed to you today. Praise God for His word. Pray the passage over your own life or someone you love. Ask God to help you live out your applications.

SOAK God's word into your heart and squeeze every bit of nourishment you can out of each day's scripture reading. Soon you will find your life transformed by the renewing of your mind!

Walk with the King!

Courtney

WomenLivingWell.org, GoodMorningGirls.org

Join the GMG Community

Share your daily SOAK on **Facebook.com/GoodMorningGirlsWLW**

Instagram: WomenLivingWell #GoodMorningGirls

GMG Bible Coloring Chart

COLORS	KEYWORDS
PURPLE	God, Jesus, Holy Spirit, Saviour, Messiah
PINK	women of the Bible, family, marriage, parenting, friendship, relationships
RED	love, kindness, mercy, compassion, peace, grace
GREEN	faith, obedience, growth, fruit, salvation, fellowship, repentance
YELLOW	worship, prayer, praise, doctrine, angels, miracles,power of God, blessings
BLUE	wisdom, teaching, instruction, commands
ORANGE	prophecy, history, times, places, kings, genealogies, people, numbers, covenants, vows, visions, oaths, future
BROWN/GRAY	Satan, sin, death, hell, evil, idols, false teachers, hypocrisy, temptation

Introduction to the Book of Psalms

Down through the centuries, believers have turned to the book of Psalms, as their favorite book of the Bible. Do you need encouragement, comfort, guidance, healing, courage or joy?

Read the book of Psalms.

The depth of emotion expressed by the writers makes this book relatable, encouraging, and comforting. It is a collection of poems, hymns, songs and prayers. They express deep and sincere faith in the midst of trials and tribulations.

The Hebrew word for "psalms" means "to pluck". This implies that the Psalms were to be accompanied by a stringed instrument. The poetic rhythm and figurative language used, clearly expresses the emotion the writer was feeling.

In the New Testament, believers are instructed to sing psalms:

> Ephesians 5:19 says, *"address one another in **psalms** and hymns and spiritual songs, singing and making melody to the Lord with your heart."*

> Colossians 3:16 says, *"Let the word of Christ dwell in you richly, teaching and admonishing one another in all wisdom, singing **psalms** and hymns and spiritual songs, with thankfulness in your hearts to God."*

Though this book was written many years ago, it is still relevant to believers today.

The Purpose: The book of Psalms was to be used as a hymnbook to sing praises to God. The word psalms is associated with playing instruments to accompany these songs.

The Author: The name of the author is at the start of each psalm. David is the most frequent writer. Other authors include: Solomon, Moses, the Sons of Korah, Asaph, Ethan and Ezahite. Some psalms have no designated author.

Time Period: This book was written between 1410-450 B.C.

Key Verse: Psalm 119:105

Your word is a lamp to my feet and a light to my path.

The Outline:

Originally, the book of Psalms was divided into 5 different books according to what was found within them.

- Book 1—Psalms 1-41
- Book 2—Psalms 42-72
- Book 3—Psalms 73-89
- Book 4—Psalms 90-106
- Book 5—Psalms 107-150

Types of Psalms:

- Psalms of Thanksgiving and Praise
- Psalms of Lament
- Psalms of Meditation, Prayer and Petition
- Psalms of Confidence and Trust
- Wisdom Psalms that Teach
- Historical Psalms
- Psalms of Suffering and Tears
- Imprecatory Psalms—Psalms that invoke judgment on their enemies.
- Kingship Psalms—Psalms that point to the future Messiah—the King of Kings or speak of David as a king.
- Acrostic Psalms—These psalms are written with special patterns using the Hebrew alphabet.

The book of Psalms is a hymnal, a prayer book, and a training guide. Every emotion a man can have is expressed from joy and sadness to anger, fear, doubt, repentance, praise, and trust. If you've felt it, Psalms expresses it. We could spend the rest of our lives reading the book of Psalms over and over and still not mine the depth of all that this book offers.

So let's get started!

Keep walking with the King!

Courtney

I will walk with integrity of heart

within my house;

I will not set before my eyes

anything that is worthless.

Psalm 101:2, 3

Reflection Question:

Integrity starts in the home. Who we are at home is who we really are. David knew that lust began with the eyes and so he needed to discipline himself to not set before his eyes anything that was wicked.

Reflect on this past week and all of the things your eyes saw. Think about the movies, television, social media and other things you have watched. Was anything dishonoring to God? If you have not set parameters for yourself, think through what your standards should be going forward and write them below.

Psalm 101

S—The S stands for *Scripture*

O—The O stands for *Observation*

A—The A stands for *Application*

K—The K stands for *Kneeling in Prayer*

But you, O Lord,

are enthroned forever;

you are remembered

throughout all generations.

Psalm 102:12

Reflection Question:

Our lives are short, like an evening shadow but God is enthroned forever! He laid the foundations of the earth and will not change. He is self-sustaining and remains forever. His influence is constant throughout all generations.

So much of life is filled with change and is out of our control. How does knowing that we have a God who is unchanging, whose word is always true and that he is a God who is with us forever, comfort you?

Psalm 102

S—The S stands for *Scripture*

O—The O stands for *Observation*

A—The A stands for *Application*

K—The K stands for *Kneeling in Prayer*

As far as the east is from the west,

so far does he remove

our transgressions from us.

Psalm 103:12

Reflection Question:

"God does not deal with us according to our sins, nor repay us according to our iniquities." (verse 10). Instead, he completely forgives us and has removed our sins as far as east is from the west. If you traveled south on a globe you would eventually be going north, but east and west never meet. If you go east on a globe, you can go east forever.

Just as east and west never meet, God completely removes our sin from us. This is how great his grace and mercy towards us is! Do you struggle to believe that God has forgiven you of a certain sin? Even though we cannot escape the consequences of some sins, we must trust that God has removed all of our sin, every single one, from us. How does this truth set you free today?

Psalm 103

S—The S stands for *Scripture*

O—The O stands for *Observation*

A—The A stands for *Application*

K—The K stands for *Kneeling in Prayer*

Bless the Lord, O my soul!

O Lord my God, you are very great!

Psalm 104:1

Reflection Question:

In this Psalm, we see the greatness of God through the splendor and majesty of his creation. God's invisible qualities, like his kindness and omnipresence, are displayed as we see how God cares for both man and the animals.

Our God is an awesome God. Nothing in all creation compares to his greatness. Pause for a moment and look out your window. Write down a few things you see and how it points to the greatness of God. Then bless the Lord with all of your soul through an act of worship in song or prayer.

S—The S stands for *Scripture*

O—The O stands for *Observation*

A—The A stands for *Application*

K—The K stands for *Kneeling in Prayer*

Seek the Lord and his strength;

seek his presence continually!

Psalm 105:4

Reflection Question:

Psalm 104 showed the majesty of God in creation and Psalm 105 shows the majesty of God in how he cares for his people. God has done wonderful things for us and we are to make his deeds known and sing praises to him. Then, we are told to seek three things: the Lord, his strength and his presence.

What are you seeking after? Are you seeking the Lord? It is easy to forget all that God has done for us in the past. But we must remember what he has done and let that remembrance strengthen us. How does God's presence strengthen you?

S—The S stands for *Scripture*

O—The O stands for *Observation*

A—The A stands for *Application*

K—The K stands for *Kneeling in Prayer*

Yet he saved them for his name's sake,

that he might make known

his mighty power.

Psalm 106:8

Reflection Question:

God's steadfast love endured towards Israel, even when they were unfaithful, ungrateful and in rebellion. God displayed his love by rescuing but then Israel repeated their sin and forgot what God had done for them. Nevertheless, God heard their cries and kept his covenant to them.

God's mighty power is seen by his great love toward his people, even when they are not in obedience to him. Have you ever fallen away from the Lord and lived in rebellion or been unfaithful to him? How did God display his mercy, love and faithfulness toward you, during that time?

Psalm 106

S—The S stands for *Scripture*

O—The O stands for *Observation*

A—The A stands for *Application*

K—The K stands for *Kneeling in Prayer*

Whoever is wise,

let him attend to these things;

let them consider

the steadfast love of the Lord.

Psalm 107:43

Reflection Question:

Those who are wise will take the time to look at the way God has dealt with man in the past. The wise man sees how God has the transforming power to make bad things good and good things bad. The wise man also notes how merciful the constant love of God is toward his children.

Let's be wise. Take a moment to pause, ponder and consider the works of the Lord in this passage. Then consider in your own life, how have you experienced the steadfast love of the Lord?

Psalm 107

S—The S stands for *Scripture*

O—The O stands for *Observation*

A—The A stands for *Application*

K—The K stands for *Kneeling in Prayer*

With God we shall do valiantly;

it is he who will tread down our foes.

Psalm 108:13

Reflection Question:

David knew that he could not avoid the battles he was facing. He had to fight, but the victory was in God's hands. He was sure that through God, they would do valiantly, and this was a reason for courage.

Is there something in your life that is requiring courage? We must not be passive or afraid of the hard things that God calls us to do. How does knowing that God is with you, give you strength to move forward in faith?

Psalm 108

S—The S stands for *Scripture*

O—The O stands for *Observation*

A—The A stands for *Application*

K—The K stands for *Kneeling in Prayer*

Be not silent,

O God of my praise!

Psalm 109:1

Reflection Question:

This is a unique Psalm where David is praying for curses against an enemy who has falsely accused him of wrongdoing. In his pain, he asks the Lord to not remain silent but rather reverse the situation and let those who are accusing him, be the ones who face ruin.

David did not take vengeance into his hands against his enemy, even though he could have. Instead, he asked the Lord to help him. Romans 12:19 says, *"Beloved, never avenge yourselves, but leave it to the wrath of God, for it is written, 'Vengeance is mine, I will repay, says the Lord.'"* Is there someone who has hurt you and you feel tempted to get revenge? Pray and ask the Lord for protection from that person and leave revenge in God's hands.

Psalm 109

S—The S stands for *Scripture*

O—The O stands for *Observation*

A—The A stands for *Application*

K—The K stands for *Kneeling in Prayer*

The Lord says to my Lord:

"Sit at my right hand,

until I make your enemies your footstool."

Psalm 110:1

Reflection Question:

Psalm 110 is one of the most quoted Old Testament chapters in the New Testament. This chapter is a prophetic Psalm revealing the Messiah in the Old Testament. While it is referring to the literal kingship of David, it points to the coming of the promised Messiah. Jesus' work was finished on the cross and so God the Father, told God the Son, to take his throne at the right hand of God.

From the days of David, through the days of the arrival of the Messiah, to our days now—God is in complete control. He will return again and judge the nations. How does seeing prophecy fulfilled and God's authority over all that takes place, encourage you?

Psalm 110

S—The S stands for *Scripture*

O—The O stands for *Observation*

A—The A stands for *Application*

K—The K stands for *Kneeling in Prayer*

*The fear of the Lord
is the beginning of wisdom;
all those who practice it
have a good understanding.*

Psalm 111:10

Reflection Question:

Wisdom does not begin until we have a proper regard and reverence for God. When we consider our creator and all of his great works, we should stand in awe of him. As a result, our understanding should lead to putting into practice obedience to his word.\

Many seek after money, pleasure and success, but what are you seeking after? Pause and consider—do you have a proper regard and reverence for God? In what area of your life do you need to practice more wisdom?

Psalm 111

S—The S stands for *Scripture*

O—The O stands for *Observation*

A—The A stands for *Application*

K—The K stands for *Kneeling in Prayer*

For the righteous

will never be moved.

Psalm 112:6

Reflection Question:

Those who fix their feet firmly on the steady rock of God, will not be moved. They do not fear trouble because they know that God is with them and he will see them through. Their hearts are firm, trusting in the Lord.

When trials come, the depth of our roots in God are revealed. How deep are your roots? Is there an area where you have been shaken? If you have slipped, return to God and go deeper with him. He loves you and wants to be your steady rock.

Psalm 112

S—The S stands for *Scripture*

O—The O stands for *Observation*

A—The A stands for *Application*

K—The K stands for *Kneeling in Prayer*

From the rising of the sun to its setting,

the name of the Lord is to be praised!

Psalm 113:3

Reflection Question:

Morning, noon and night, our God is worthy of praise. He is unchanging and always worthy of continual praise.

List 5 things you can praise the Lord for today and then pause and give him praise right where you are. He is worthy.

Psalm 113

S—The S stands for *Scripture*

O—The O stands for *Observation*

A—The A stands for *Application*

K—The K stands for *Kneeling in Prayer*

Tremble, O earth,

at the presence of the Lord.

Psalm 114:7

Reflection Question:

The Lord is the Lord of all the earth. Not only are we called to fear him, but all creation trembles at his mighty and majestic presence.

Imagine being in the presence of the Lord in heaven. What sort of emotions do you think you will feel? How does knowing that the God, who causes the whole earth to tremble, loves you deeply and is with you and for you?

Psalm 114

S—The S stands for *Scripture*

O—The O stands for *Observation*

A—The A stands for *Application*

K—The K stands for *Kneeling in Prayer*

Not to us, O Lord, not to us,

but to your name give glory.

Psalm 115:1

Reflection Question:

God works through his people, but twice we are told the glory is not for us. We are to magnify the Lord and give him all the glory that is due his name.

It is so easy to forget how God is helping us and enabling us to do the things we do. Is there an area where you take for granted your skill or abilities and have grown prideful? Take a moment to humble yourself before the Lord and give his name glory, for the gifts and talents and great things he has done in your life.

Psalm 115

S—The S stands for *Scripture*

O—The O stands for *Observation*

A—The A stands for *Application*

K—The K stands for *Kneeling in Prayer*

Precious in the sight of the Lord

is the death of his saints.

Psalm 116:15

Reflection Question:

God is close to his people as they stand at death's door. Sometimes he intervenes and saves his people from death and other times, he takes them home. Eventually, every saint dies. The death of a saint is precious in the eyes of the Lord because finally they are together in perfect fellowship.

Death is no small thing for God. He knows the number of days we will live. Are you fearful of death? How does knowing that God is close to you until your last breath and will see your death as precious, a comfort to you?

Psalm 116

S—The S stands for *Scripture*

O—The O stands for *Observation*

A—The A stands for *Application*

K—The K stands for *Kneeling in Prayer*

Praise the Lord, all nations!

Extol him, all peoples!

Psalm 117:1

Reflection Question:

God's love is not just for Israel but for all of the nations. He loves both the Jews and Gentiles. That steadfast love reaches all of our hearts and should cause us to praise Him!

God is faithful and worthy of all our praise for many reasons. One of those reasons is his love for all the nations. How have you seen God's love for the nations displayed? If you know the name of a missionary, say a prayer for them today as they proclaim the love of Jesus around the world.

Psalm 117

S—The S stands for *Scripture*

O—The O stands for *Observation*

A—The A stands for *Application*

K—The K stands for *Kneeling in Prayer*

It is better to take refuge in the Lord

than to trust in man.

Psalm 118:8

Reflection Question:

There is no one more trustworthy than God. There are some that can help, but won't and others who want to help, but can't. God is wiser, stronger, safer and more dependable than any person can ever be. It is better to take refuge in the Lord than to trust in a person.

While we all need people we can trust in our lives, this Psalm says it is better to trust in the Lord. If you have faced disappointment from someone you trusted, then you know how painful it can be to be betrayed or rejected. God will never betray or reject you. You can fully trust him. How has God proven himself to be a safe and trusted refuge in your life?

Psalm 118

S—The S stands for *Scripture*

O—The O stands for *Observation*

A—The A stands for *Application*

K—The K stands for *Kneeling in Prayer*

Your word is a lamp to my feet

and a light to my path.

Psalm 119:105

Reflection Question:

When a lamp is turned on in a dark room it brings comfort, light and clarity. God's word is to be our light in this dark world. If we will read it and follow it, God will guide our steps and lead the way.

Every day we turn on lights in our house. In the same way, every day we need to turn to the light of God's word to give us wisdom and clarity for life. But God doesn't promise to light our entire path, sometimes he only gives us enough light for the next step. How has God's word been a light in the darkness in your life? And how does God's word guide your steps?

Psalm 119

S—The S stands for *Scripture*

O—The O stands for *Observation*

A—The A stands for *Application*

K—The K stands for *Kneeling in Prayer*

In my distress I called to the Lord,

and he answered me.

Psalm 120:1

Reflection Question:

God is faithful. He is a God who hears our prayers. He hears our cries for help in the midst of distress and he delivers his people.

Have you ever cried out for help and felt like God did not deliver you? I have. But now that I look back at those times, I am able to see that God was working something else out in my life that I could not understand in that moment and he truly did hear my cries. Is there something stressing you out right now? Tell God about right now and ask him for help. Then wait on the Lord and trust that he does hear the prayers of his people. God loves you!

Psalm 120

S—The S stands for *Scripture*

O—The O stands for *Observation*

A—The A stands for *Application*

K—The K stands for *Kneeling in Prayer*

He who keeps you

will not slumber.

Psalm 121:3

Reflection Question:

Like a guard who watches over a city at night, our God does not sleep. He is always watching over us and protecting us.

We do not serve a sleepy God! Do you sometimes struggle to sleep at night? How does knowing that God is awake and watching over you all night long, give you peace, so you can rest?

Psalm 121

S—The S stands for *Scripture*

O—The O stands for *Observation*

A—The A stands for *Application*

K—The K stands for *Kneeling in Prayer*

I was glad when they said to me,

"Let us go to the house of the Lord!"

Psalm 122:1

Reflection Question:

David was happy to be invited to join others in the house of the Lord. There they could pray, worship and fellowship together.

While the church is the people, not the building, the church building is a place where God's people meet together. It is good for us to be with God's people in the house of the Lord. Do you have a church you attend regularly? No church is perfect because all churches are filled with imperfect people, but in what ways do you find joy in going to your church?

Psalm 122

S—The S stands for *Scripture*

O—The O stands for *Observation*

A—The A stands for *Application*

K—The K stands for *Kneeling in Prayer*

Have mercy upon us, O Lord,

have mercy upon us.

Psalm 123:3

Reflection Question:

The Psalmist begged the Lord for mercy. In desperation, he didn't ask just once. He asked twice and he continued to look to the Lord and wait on him until he received the mercy he asked for.

Is there something you need from the Lord today? Write your request below and then don't just ask once—continue to ask and watch and wait on the Lord to answer your prayer.

Psalm 123

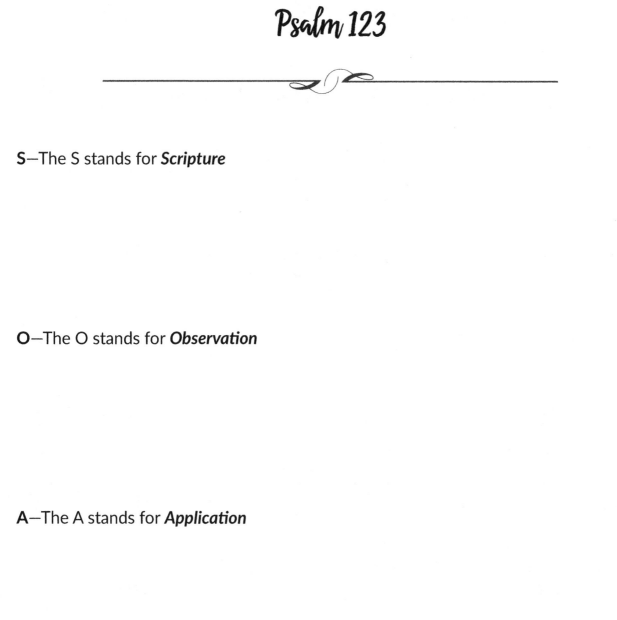

S—The S stands for *Scripture*

O—The O stands for *Observation*

A—The A stands for *Application*

K—The K stands for *Kneeling in Prayer*

Our help is in the name of the Lord,

who made heaven and earth.

Psalm 124:8

Reflection Question:

We can be confident that the maker of the heavens and the earth is with us. When we call on his name, he will help us.

It is no small thing to have access to the maker of the heavens and earth! Our confidence that we can call on him and he will help us, should be secure. Remembering past times that God helped us, grows our trust. Think back over your life and tell of a time when you prayed and asked the Lord for help. How did he answer that prayer?

Psalm 124

S—The S stands for *Scripture*

O—The O stands for *Observation*

A—The A stands for *Application*

K—The K stands for *Kneeling in Prayer*

Those who trust in the Lord

are like Mount Zion,

which cannot be moved,

but abides forever.

Psalm 125:1

Reflection Question:

Our trust in the Lord makes us strong and secure. Even though life may bring hard times, like a firmly established mountain, we will not be moved and will abide forever.

We cannot be strong and secure until we put our complete trust in God. What are you trusting in today? Are you trusting in yourself and your own strength or in God's? Is there something that is competing with God for your dependency? Confess and realign your heart with God's today.

S—The S stands for *Scripture*

O—The O stands for *Observation*

A—The A stands for *Application*

K—The K stands for *Kneeling in Prayer*

Those who sow in tears

shall reap with shouts of joy!

Psalm 126:5

Reflection Question:

Our tears are like seeds. It is okay to cry before the Lord in prayer as we wait on him to answer. Though relief may not come quickly, in time, joy will return. And it won't just be a little joy—it will be so much you want to shout for joy.

Our emotions are involved in our faith. Sometimes we may become discouraged and find ourselves in tears as we try to trust in God. If we continue to trust, even through the hard times, we will reap joy. What have you been struggling with lately, that has brought you to tears? How does the hope of joy encourage you in your season of waiting?

S—The S stands for *Scripture*

O—The O stands for *Observation*

A—The A stands for *Application*

K—The K stands for *Kneeling in Prayer*

It is in vain that you rise up early

and go late to rest,

eating the bread of anxious toil;

for he gives to his beloved sleep.

Psalm 127:2

Reflection Question:

Hard work is important but if our trust is in our work, rather than the Lord, it will lead to anxiety and sorrows. Work is unending. There will always be more to do, but those who rely on the Lord can stop and rest. They can sleep peacefully knowing that the Lord is in control.

Do you need more sleep? Is your lack of sleep being caused by working too much? In what area of your life are you feeling anxious? How can you trust God more with this area of your life?

Psalm 127

S—The S stands for *Scripture*

O—The O stands for *Observation*

A—The A stands for *Application*

K—The K stands for *Kneeling in Prayer*

Blessed is everyone who fears the Lord,

who walks in his ways!

Psalm 128:1

Reflection Question:

While fearing God is an attitude of heart and an emotion, walking in God's ways is a matter of obedience. The fear of the Lord should lead to obedience, which then leads to blessing.

The word blessed means happy. Everyone is ultimately seeking happiness and God's word tells us how to find it, by fearing God and walking in his ways. In what ways do you tend to seek happiness? Perhaps it's in comfort, food, fun, relationships, money, or success. While those are blessings from God that bring happiness, sometimes we can get sidetracked and focus more on the gifts from God than from the giver of the gifts. How has God blessed you because of your obedience? Praise the giver for these good gifts today.

Psalm 128

S—The S stands for *Scripture*

O—The O stands for *Observation*

A—The A stands for *Application*

K—The K stands for *Kneeling in Prayer*

The blessing of the Lord

be upon you!

Psalm 129:8

Reflection Question:

The history of Israel is one of suffering, as they have been afflicted by their enemies since the beginning of their nation. In this Psalm, the psalmist was praying that the good blessings of God would be withheld from their enemies. He wanted God to withhold his goodness from them because of the way they had hated Israel.

Israel had suffered pain from their enemies but not defeat. In the midst of their pain, they prayed. They prayed in verse 5 that their enemies would be turned around. Is there someone hurting you today? It is okay and even good to pray that the Lord would stop them and turn them around. Jesus commands us to love our enemies and to pray for them. So, pause right now and write a prayer below for someone who is either hurting you or hurting a loved one. Pray that the Lord would turn their life around.

Psalm 129

S—The S stands for *Scripture*

O—The O stands for *Observation*

A—The A stands for *Application*

K—The K stands for *Kneeling in Prayer*

I wait for the Lord,

my soul waits,

and in his word I hope.

Psalm 130:5

Reflection Question:

As the Psalmist waited on the Lord, he did not wait passively. He trusted in God's promises and actively waited with hope.

Verse 6 says he waited as a watchman waits for the morning. A watchman does not doubt that the morning will come. He knows it's coming and is watching for it. Is there an area in your life where you are waiting on the Lord? Are you waiting passively, stuck in a cycle of doubt or actively waiting with hope?

Psalm 130

S—The S stands for *Scripture*

O—The O stands for *Observation*

A—The A stands for *Application*

K—The K stands for *Kneeling in Prayer*

I have calmed

and quieted my soul.

Psalm 131:2

Reflection Question:

God did not calm and quiet David's soul, David had to choose to calm and quiet his soul. Like a weaned child enjoys the close relationship of his mother, David enjoyed his close relationship with God and was content in his presence.

God loves us like a mother cares and protects her little ones. Are you enjoying your walk with God? How can you become calmer and quieter in his presence?

Psalm 131

S—The S stands for **Scripture**

O—The O stands for **Observation**

A—The A stands for **Application**

K—The K stands for **Kneeling in Prayer**

Let us go to his dwelling place;

let us worship at his footstool!

Psalm 132:7

Reflection Question:

David endured many hardships as he sought to follow God and God promised that he would establish David's throne forever. That promise was fulfilled through Jesus the Messiah.

Just as God kept his promise to David, God keeps his promises to us. How does knowing that we have a God who keeps all of his promises, from Genesis to Revelation, build your faith and joy?

S—The S stands for *Scripture*

O—The O stands for *Observation*

A—The A stands for *Application*

K—The K stands for *Kneeling in Prayer*

Behold, how good and pleasant it is

when brothers dwell in unity!

Psalm 133:1

Reflection Question:

Behold means to pay attention and watch. We are to pay attention to how good and pleasant unity is. Unity is good because it pleases the Lord and it is pleasant because it makes life sweeter.

God wants us to have unity in the church. Being unified is being together in Spirit rather than divided. Have you experienced this sweetness? Sometimes conflict or hurt feelings can break up the unity. How can you show more love and more grace in the family of God so that you can experience the blessings of unity?

Psalm 133

S—The S stands for *Scripture*

O—The O stands for *Observation*

A—The A stands for *Application*

K—The K stands for *Kneeling in Prayer*

May the Lord bless you from Zion,

he who made heaven and earth!

Psalm 134:3

Reflection Question:

As we bless and praise God, he blesses us. The Lord's blessings are not just for the church as a whole but for each of us as an individual and it is for all of his children everywhere.

This Psalm is a call to worship and the act of praising the Lord is a blessing in and of itself. So, let's bless the Lord right now and receive his blessings as we do it. Write a word of praise below and then pause and sing a song of worship to him right where you are?

S—The S stands for *Scripture*

O—The O stands for *Observation*

A—The A stands for *Application*

K—The K stands for *Kneeling in Prayer*

Praise the Lord,

for the Lord is good;

sing to his name,

for it is pleasant!

Psalm 135:3

Reflection Question:

We do not just praise God because he is God but also because he is good. One of the ways we praise God is through song. The people of God should be a people who sing together.

The benefits of singing to the Lord are not just for God, but for us as well. Singing is pleasant and is a comfort to our souls. What is your favorite worship song and why is it your favorite?

Psalm 135

S—The S stands for **Scripture**

O—The O stands for **Observation**

A—The A stands for **Application**

K—The K stands for **Kneeling in Prayer**

Give thanks to the Lord,

for he is good,

for his steadfast love

endures forever.

Psalm 136:1

Reflection Question:

In this Psalm, 26 times we are told that God's steadfast love endures forever. It will never end! We must give thanks to the Lord because his mercy and loyal devotion is forever and ever.

Consider how wonderful God's love is for you. It will never ever end. He is so good! Now write a prayer of thanksgiving to God below.

S—The S stands for *Scripture*

O—The O stands for *Observation*

A—The A stands for *Application*

K—The K stands for *Kneeling in Prayer*

How shall we sing the Lord's song

in a foreign land?

Psalm 137:4

Reflection Question:

In this Psalm, the people of Israel are in despair because they have been taken into exile. All of their singing and praise has stopped, and they are praying for justice to come on their enemies.

Our God is good and worthy of all of our praise but sometimes life's storms bring us low. Tell of a time when you were in such despair you could not lift your voice to sing in worship? How did God bring you through this difficult time?

Psalm 137

S—The S stands for *Scripture*

O—The O stands for *Observation*

A—The A stands for *Application*

K—The K stands for *Kneeling in Prayer*

The Lord will fulfill

his purpose for me.

Psalm 138:8

Reflection Question:

David was confident that God had a purpose for him and that he would fulfill that purpose. God promised that David's throne would be established forever and that was fulfilled through the Messiah.

God has a perfect plan for you and while the twists and turns of life may not always feel perfect, God is good, and we can trust in his perfect plan for us. Philippians 1:6 says, *"And I am sure of this, that he who began a good work in you will bring it to completion at the day of Jesus Christ."* How does this truth give you hope?

Psalm 138

S—The S stands for *Scripture*

O—The O stands for *Observation*

A—The A stands for *Application*

K—The K stands for *Kneeling in Prayer*

I praise you, for I am fearfully and wonderfully made.

Psalm 139:14

Reflection Question:

When you study the human body and all of the intricacies of its design, you realize how incredible your body is. We have an amazing and brilliant creator who not only gave us this wonderful body but also gave us a soul and spirit, so that we can connect with him.

God knew you before you were born and knit you together in your mother's womb. You are wonderfully and fearfully made. You are valuable and your creator loves you. All of God's creation is wonderful—including you! Do you know and believe this deep in your soul? How has the enemy lied to you and tried to make you believe otherwise? Write that lie below and then cross it out and write the truth below it.

Psalm 139

S—The S stands for **Scripture**

O—The O stands for **Observation**

A—The A stands for **Application**

K—The K stands for **Kneeling in Prayer**

Guard me, O Lord,

from the hands of the wicked.

Psalm 140:4

Reflection Question:

Most likely this Psalm was written during a time of war and David was praying that the Lord would protect him from his enemies. David was hunted down by his enemies like a man hunts a wild animal. He was frequently in danger and knew that he needed the Lord on his side for protection. And though this Psalm starts out with David in fear, it ends with David confident that God would rescue him.

One of the ways the godly face persecution is by having their words twisted, or their intentions questioned. Sometimes they are lied about, slandered, or lured into a trap of temptation, just so they can be brought down. Is there someone in your life who is opposed to you right now? Write a prayer below asking the Lord to guard you from this person and their attacks or snares?

S—The S stands for *Scripture*

O—The O stands for *Observation*

A—The A stands for *Application*

K—The K stands for *Kneeling in Prayer*

Set a guard, O Lord,

over my mouth;

keep watch over the

door of my lips!

Psalm 141:3

Reflection Question:

David humbly asked the Lord to put a guard over his mouth. He wanted his lips to be used for prayer and praise and not for lies, slander or complaining. He knew he needed the help of the Lord to control his words and be like a guard over the door of his lips.

Our lips are like a door that opens and closes. James 3:10 says, "From the same mouth come blessing and cursing. My brothers, these things ought not to be so." In what ways do you struggle to control your words? Do you struggle with gossip, complaining, lying, slander or swearing? Pray and ask the Lord to help guard your lips from saying these things?

Psalm 141

S—The S stands for **Scripture**

O—The O stands for **Observation**

A—The A stands for **Application**

K—The K stands for **Kneeling in Prayer**

When my spirit faints within me,

you know my way!

Psalm 142:3

Reflection Question:

David wrote this Psalm in a cave when he was overwhelmed and exhausted. And though David knew that the enemies were surrounding him, he could say with confidence that God would provide a way out.

Even David who killed the giant Goliath, grew weary and tired and unsure of the path he was on. Are you tired and weary today? Do you feel unsure of your future? Tell God how you feel. How does knowing that God is with you every step of the way and that he already knows the path you will take, give you peace and strength to press on for another day?

Psalm 142

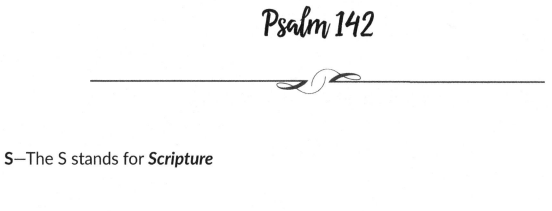

S—The S stands for *Scripture*

O—The O stands for *Observation*

A—The A stands for *Application*

K—The K stands for *Kneeling in Prayer*

Let me hear in the morning

of your steadfast love,

for in you I trust.

Psalm 143:8

Reflection Question:

David was listening to hear the voice of God. Every morning, he woke up and turned to God in prayer. He needed to be reassured of God's love, as he trusted in him for whatever the day had in store.

Sometimes we may go to bed feeling discouraged and defeated, but every night comes to an end and the morning returns again. What is your morning routine? Are you listening to God in the morning? Are you turning to God and being reminded of his steadfast love at the start of the day? How would this change your life if you did this daily?

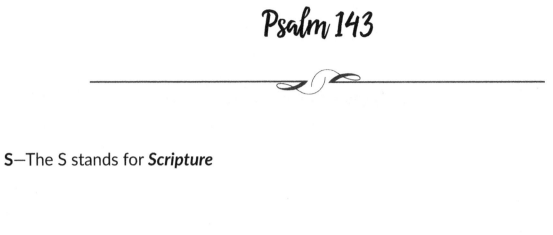

Psalm 143

S—The S stands for *Scripture*

O—The O stands for *Observation*

A—The A stands for *Application*

K—The K stands for *Kneeling in Prayer*

Blessed be the Lord,

my rock.

Psalm 144:1

Reflection Question:

David is in the midst of a battle, but he is calm because he can call on the Lord. He says God is his rock, fortress, stronghold, deliverer and refuge -- but before he gives the Lord those titles, he mentions God's steadfast love. It was God's steadfast love that gave him his strength and ability to be a skilled warrior.

Is God your rock, fortress, stronghold, deliverer and refuge? And how does remembering God's love, as the first among the list of all the names of God, make your relationship with God more personal?

Psalm 144

S—The S stands for **Scripture**

O—The O stands for **Observation**

A—The A stands for **Application**

K—The K stands for **Kneeling in Prayer**

The Lord is near
to all who call on him,
to all who call on him in truth.

Psalm 145:18

Reflection Question:

Our God is near, and he hears the cries of his people for help. Some who cry out to God, do not know him. They only cry out for selfish reasons rather than being followers of his truth. But God is always near to his people when they pray.

The Lord is gracious and good to all but there is a special, personal relationship he has with his people. What does it mean to you to know that God is always near to you? How can you practice the presence and nearness of God more in your life?

Psalm 145

S—The S stands for *Scripture*

O—The O stands for *Observation*

A—The A stands for *Application*

K—The K stands for *Kneeling in Prayer*

Praise the Lord,

O my soul!

I will praise the Lord

as long as I live.

Psalm 146:1, 2

Reflection Question:

Praise is not meant to be a dull routine of repetition. Instead, as we receive new mercies from God each day and learn new things about his love and grace, our songs should be fresh and new, so that we can sing them all of our lives.

Have you fallen into a boring routine of singing the same songs over and over? What new things have you experienced or learned about God, that you can celebrate? How does this revive your worship?

S—The S stands for *Scripture*

O—The O stands for *Observation*

A—The A stands for *Application*

K—The K stands for *Kneeling in Prayer*

He heals the brokenhearted

and binds up their wounds.

Psalm 147:3

Reflection Question:

David knew what it felt like to be broken hearted. He had been wounded by betrayal, but God had healed him. The same God that numbers the stars and knows them by name, cared about David's broken heart and tended to his wounds.

Are you hurting today? Has someone broken your heart or wounded you? The Lord cares and he loves you so much. He is near to you. He wants to heal you. Ask him for healing today.

S—The S stands for *Scripture*

O—The O stands for *Observation*

A—The A stands for *Application*

K—The K stands for *Kneeling in Prayer*

Let them praise the name of the Lord,

for his name alone is exalted;

his majesty is above earth and heaven.

Psalm 148:13

Reflection Question:

The Psalmist calls on all of creation to praise the name of the Lord. He calls on the angels, sun, moon, stars, waters, sea creatures, fire, hail, snow, wind, mountains, trees, livestock, birds and more to praise him. Then he calls on all the people of the earth, both the princes and the young children, to praise the Lord.

Our praise to the Lord must not be silent. Sometimes our worship is soft and quiet but other times it should be enthusiastic. All the earth is commanded to praise the Lord. Are you comfortable being noisy in your worship? Why or why not? How can you be freer with your worship this week?

Psalm 148

S—The S stands for *Scripture*

O—The O stands for *Observation*

A—The A stands for *Application*

K—The K stands for *Kneeling in Prayer*

Let them praise his name with dancing,

making melody to him with tambourine and lyre!

For the Lord takes pleasure in his people.

Psalm 149:3,4

Reflection Question:

The Psalmist invites God's people to sing and dance and play instruments with great joy to the Lord. God takes pleasure in the praise of his people.

Do you ever judge others who are a little over the top with their praise? Or have you felt constrained by what others might think of you, if you lift your hands and sing out in worship? Have you ever considered how much God loves it when you let loose and just praise him with all of your heart and soul? How does knowing that God takes pleasure in your praise, encourage you to enjoy worship more, despite what others might think?

Psalm 149

S—The S stands for *Scripture*

O—The O stands for *Observation*

A—The A stands for *Application*

K—The K stands for *Kneeling in Prayer*

Let everything that has breath

praise the Lord!

Praise the Lord!

Psalm 150:6

Reflection Question:

The book of Psalms ends with a final call for everything that has breath, to praise the Lord. God is the giver of every breath, so it is only appropriate that the creation praises the creator.

Our God is good, gracious, forgiving and full of mercy. He is our refuge and strength and always near to us when we call on his name. His steadfast love endures and because of his faithfulness and our salvation, we can give thanks to Him and praise His name forever! And so, one last time, as we finish the book of Psalms, let's praise the Lord. Sing a song or write a poem of praise to the Lord below and keep walking with the King!

Psalm 150

S—The S stands for *Scripture*

O—The O stands for *Observation*

A—The A stands for *Application*

K—The K stands for *Kneeling in Prayer*

Made in the USA
Coppell, TX
15 May 2020